BLANK COMIC BOOK FOR KIDS

SHORT STORY AND ARTWORK

KSENIJA KUKULE

DREAM. INSPIRE. CREATE.

VISIT US ONLINE:
www.YoungDreamersPress.com

TAG US IN YOUR PHOTOS & VIDEOS:
www.instagram.com/youngdreamerspress
www.tiktok.com/@youngdreamerspress

WE'RE ALSO ON FACEBOOK:
www.facebook.com/youngdreamerspress

ISBN-13: 978-1-990864-46-9

STEP 1: GET THE INSPIRATION
(Read other comics)

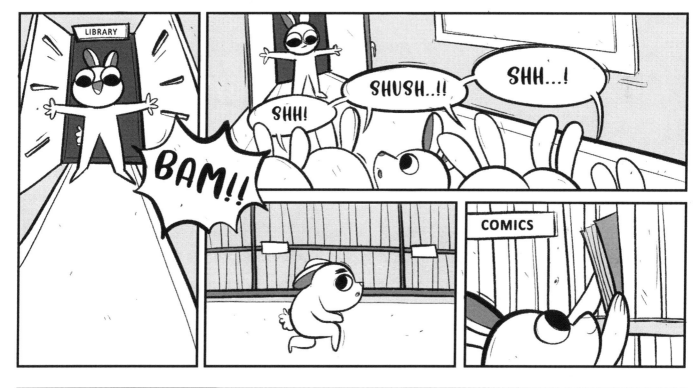

STEP 1: GET THE INSPIRATION
(Or you can watch other's art)

STEP 1: GET THE INSPIRATION
(Watch your favorite movies)

STEP 2: DRAW YOUR COMICS

STEP 3: SHARE WITH OTHERS

BUT WAIT, THERE'S MORE!

VISIT GO.YOUNGDREAMERSPRESS.COM/BLANK2

To join our newsletter and make their world more colorful with **free** printable coloring pages!

All pages sized for 8.5 x 11 paper and include a wide range of subjects including: animals, kittens, mermaids, unicorns, mandalas, an astronaut, planets, a firetruck, a construction vehicle, cupcakes, and more!

978-1-989387-13-9

978-1-989387-46-7

978-1-989387-96-2

978-1-990136-07-8

978-1-990136-04-7

978-1-990136-70-2

978-1-990136-52-8

978-1-989790-96-0

Suitable for Ages 4-8 & 9-12

978-1-990136-39-9

978-1-990136-09-2

978-1-990136-16-0

978-1-990864-47-6

978-1-990136-02-3

978-1-989790-94-6

978-1-989790-69-4

978-1-990136-01-6

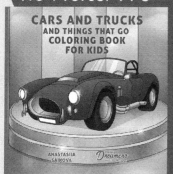

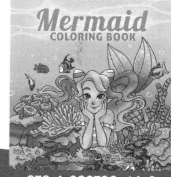

Made in the USA
Las Vegas, NV
14 December 2024

14213635R00063